Flute Exam Pieces

ABRSM Grade 5

Selected from the 2014–2017 syllabus

Piano accompaniment

C000183514

Contents

Footnotes: Anthony Burton and Rachel Brown (RB)

The pieces in this album have been taken from a variety of different sources. Where appropriate, they have been checked with original source material and edited to help the player when preparing for performance. Any editorial additions are given in small print; within square brackets; or, in the case of slurs and ties, in the form ⌒. Details of other editorial amendments or suggestions are given in the footnotes. Breath marks (retained here where they appear in the source edition) and all editorial additions are for guidance only; they are not comprehensive or obligatory. Descriptive titles are given in their original language, and translations into English appear above the footnotes.

ABRSM Flute Exams: requirements

Pieces

In the exam, candidates must play three pieces, one chosen from each of the three syllabus lists (A, B and C). Candidates are free to choose from the pieces printed in this album and/or from the other pieces set for the grade: a full list is given in the flute part with this score as well as in the 2014–2017 Woodwind syllabus.

Scales and arpeggios
Sight-reading
Aural tests

Full details are available online at www.abrsm.org/flute5 or in the 2014–2017 Woodwind syllabus booklet.

First published in 2013 by ABRSM (Publishing) Ltd, a wholly owned subsidiary of ABRSM, 24 Portland Place, London W1B 1LU, United Kingdom

© 2013 by The Associated Board of the Royal Schools of Music

Music origination by Andrew Jones
Cover by Kate Benjamin & Andy Potts
Printed in England by Caligraving Ltd, Thetford, Norfolk
Reprinted in 2013

Allegro

Second movement from Sonata in F, HWV 369, Op. 1 No. 11

Edited by and continuo
realization by Rachel Brown

G. F. Handel
(1685–1759)

The composer George Frideric Handel was born in Germany but settled in London. The Sonata in F major for recorder, from which this Allegro is taken, was published in 1732 by John Walsh as Op. 1 No. 11 and was later adapted as an organ concerto, Op. 4 No. 5. All dynamics and slurs are editorial, and therefore optional, but additional slurs could be added. Repeated notes and leaps might generally be played more detached, and step-wise movement more legato. RB

Source: autograph MS, Cambridge, Fitzwilliam Museum, MU.MS.261

Largo and Vivace

First and second movements from Sonata No. 2 in D minor

Edited by and continuo
realization by Rachel Brown

Daniel Purcell
(c.1664–1717)

Daniel Purcell, younger brother of Henry Purcell, worked as organist at Magdalen College, Oxford and as composer in residence at London's Theatre Royal in Drury Lane, but the rich homophonic texture of the grand opening movement of this sonata owes something to his early training as a boy chorister at the Chapel Royal. The oblique lines in bar 21 of the Largo movement and bar 24 of the Vivace movement probably indicate a caesura, rather like a punctuation mark at the end of a sentence. The last two trills of the Vivace (bar 26, 4th beat and bar 27) may be simplified or omitted in the exam. In bar 9 of the Vivace movement, the fifth note of the flute part is *c'''* in the source, which appears to be a mistake and has been replaced with *b''*. RB

Source: *Six Sonatas or Solos, three for a Violin, and three for the Flute, with a Through Bass for the Harpsichord* (London: Walsh, *c.*1730–66?)

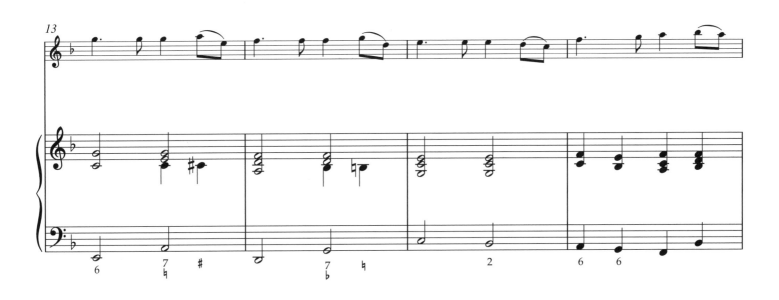

6

Presto

Third movement from Sonata in G, Op. 1 No. 6

A:3

J. J. Quantz
(1697–1773)

Edited by and continuo
realization by Rachel Brown

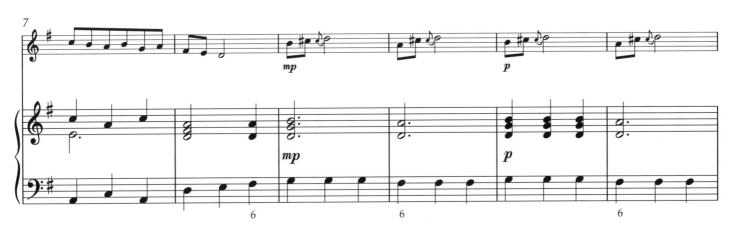

Johann Joachim Quantz is chiefly remembered for his comprehensive book on performance of Baroque music (translated as *On Playing the Flute*) and for his role as flute teacher to Frederick the Great, King of Prussia. Yet he was a colourful character, surviving an assassination attempt, being tricked into marriage and teaching Frederick in secret before he became king. Quantz was also the highly prolific composer of around three hundred flute concertos and more than two hundred flute sonatas, many of which are extremely virtuosic. All dynamics are editorial apart from those in bars 60/61 and bar 65. RB

Source: *Solos for a German flute or violin with a thorough bass for the harpsichord or violoncello* (Walsh, 1744)

Morceau

(*Concours de flûte*, 1876)

B:1

Edited by John Solum

Léo Delibes
(1836–91)

Morceau Piece; **Concours de flûte** Flute Competition

End-of-year competitions, or examinations, at the Paris Conservatoire in the 19th century included a sight-reading test, with piano accompaniment, specially written by one of the Conservatoire's professors of composition. For the 1876 flute test, the composer was Léo Delibes, best known as a composer of operas such as *Lakmé* (which includes the well-known 'Flower Duet') and ballets such as *Coppélia* and *Sylvia*. Rather than producing a piece designed to challenge the student's speed of reading or technical ability, he chose to write one which chiefly requires variations of phrasing and tone-colour to bring out the contrasting mood of the middle section (from bar 27) and coda (from bar 60).

Nobody Knows

No. 1 from *The Christopher Norton Concert Collection for Flute*

B:2

Christopher Norton
(born 1953)

Christopher Norton is a New Zealand-born, British-based composer who has specialized in educational music, including the popular 'Microjazz' series. His *Concert Collection* albums are sets of original pieces based on traditional tunes, classical themes and the songs of Stephen Foster, published with a CD containing playalong tracks. This piece in the style of a jazz improvisation is based on the spiritual 'Nobody knows the trouble I've seen', a song which would have been sung by slaves in the southern USA in the 19th century. The original melody is first heard in the piano part at bar 7. A small number of editorial adjustments to dynamics and articulation have been made without comment.

broadening   a tempo

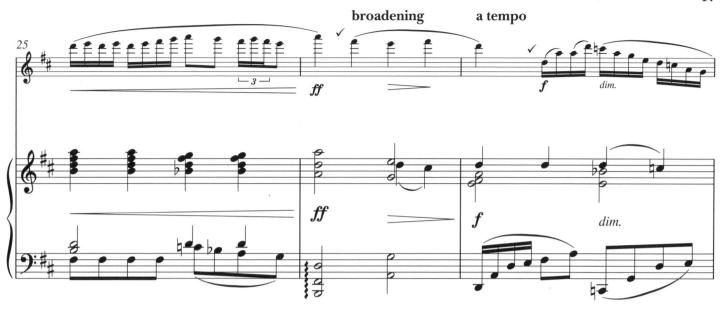

gradually broadening to the end

The Playful Pony

from *Luna's Magic Flute*

Blaž Pucihar
(born 1977)

Blaž Pucihar is a composer and pianist from Slovenia; he leads a quartet which plays the music of Bach in jazz style, and is the director of an international summer school. His wife Ana Kavčič Pucihar is a flautist, and he has written several pieces for her. *Luna's Magic Flute* is a story with music, about a girl named Luna who makes everyone she meets happy by playing her magic flute. 'The Playful Pony' is the music she plays to cheer up a sad pony. When the main tune comes back, in the piano part at the end of bar 75, the flute contributes to the accompaniment: this passage requires a different colour as well as quieter dynamics, all the way to the end of bar 91.

Flute Exam Pieces

ABRSM Grade 5

Selected from the 2014–2017 syllabus

Name

Date of exam

Contents

page

Footnotes: Anthony Burton and Rachel Brown (RB)

Other pieces for Grade 5

First published in 2013 by ABRSM (Publishing) Ltd, a wholly owned subsidiary of ABRSM, 24 Portland Place, London W1B 1LU, United Kingdom © 2013 by The Associated Board of the Royal Schools of Music

Music origination by Andrew Jones Cover by Kate Benjamin & Andy Potts Printed in England by Caligraving Ltd, Thetford, Norfolk

MIX
Paper from responsible sources
FSC™ C109619

A:1

Allegro

Second movement from Sonata in F, HWV 369, Op. 1 No. 11

Edited by and continuo
realization by Rachel Brown

G. F. Handel
(1685–1759)

The composer George Frideric Handel was born in Germany but settled in London. The Sonata in F major for recorder, from which this Allegro is taken, was published in 1732 by John Walsh as Op. 1 No. 11 and was later adapted as an organ concerto, Op. 4 No. 5. All dynamics and slurs are editorial, and therefore optional, but additional slurs could be added. Repeated notes and leaps might generally be played more detached, and step-wise movement more legato. RB

Source: autograph MS, Cambridge, Fitzwilliam Museum, MU.MS.261

AB 3681

thumb B♭

Largo and Vivace

First and second movements from Sonata No. 2 in D minor

Edited by and continuo
realization by Rachel Brown

Daniel Purcell
(c.1664–1717)

Daniel Purcell, younger brother of Henry Purcell, worked as organist at Magdalen College, Oxford and as composer in residence at London's Theatre Royal in Drury Lane, but the rich homophonic texture of the grand opening movement of this sonata owes something to his early training as a boy chorister at the Chapel Royal. The oblique lines in bar 21 of the Largo movement and bar 24 of the Vivace movement probably indicate a caesura, rather like a punctuation mark at the end of a sentence. The last two trills of the Vivace (bar 26, 4th beat and bar 27) may be simplified or omitted in the exam. In bar 9 of the Vivace movement, the fifth note of the flute part is *c'''* in the source, which appears to be a mistake and has been replaced with *b''*. RB

Source: *Six Sonatas or Solos, three for a Violin, and three for the Flute, with a Through Bass for the Harpsichord* (London: Walsh, *c.*1730–66?)

Presto

Third movement from Sonata in G, Op. 1 No. 6

Edited by and continuo
realization by Rachel Brown

J. J. Quantz
(1697–1773)

Johann Joachim Quantz is chiefly remembered for his comprehensive book on performance of Baroque music (translated as *On Playing the Flute*) and for his role as flute teacher to Frederick the Great, King of Prussia. Yet he was a colourful character, surviving an assassination attempt, being tricked into marriage and teaching Frederick in secret before he became king. Quantz was also the highly prolific composer of around three hundred flute concertos and more than two hundred flute sonatas, many of which are extremely virtuosic. All dynamics are editorial apart from those in bars 60 and 65. RB

Source: *Solos for a German flute or violin with a thorough bass for the harpsichord or violoncello* (Walsh, 1744)

Morceau

(Concours de flûte, 1876)

Edited by John Solum

Léo Delibes
(1836–91)

Morceau Piece; **Concours de flûte** Flute Competition

End-of-year competitions, or examinations, at the Paris Conservatoire in the 19th century included a sight-reading test, with piano accompaniment, specially written by one of the Conservatoire's professors of composition. For the 1876 flute test, the composer was Léo Delibes, best known as a composer of operas such as *Lakmé* (which includes the well-known 'Flower Duet') and ballets such as *Coppélia* and *Sylvia*. Rather than producing a piece designed to challenge the student's speed of reading or technical ability, he chose to write one which chiefly requires variations of phrasing and tone-colour to bring out the contrasting mood of the middle section (from bar 27) and coda (from bar 60).

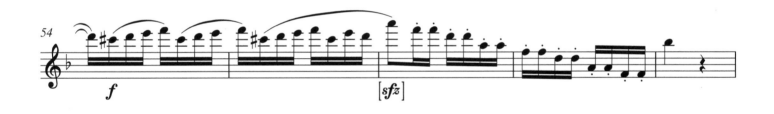

Nobody Knows

No. 1 from *The Christopher Norton Concert Collection for Flute*

Christopher Norton
(born 1953)

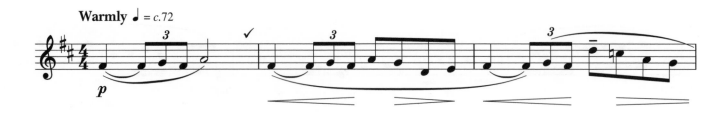

Christopher Norton is a New Zealand-born, British-based composer who has specialized in educational music, including the popular 'Microjazz' series. His *Concert Collection* albums are sets of original pieces based on traditional tunes, classical themes and the songs of Stephen Foster, published with a CD containing playalong tracks. This piece in the style of a jazz improvisation is based on the spiritual 'Nobody knows the trouble I've seen', a song which would have been sung by slaves in the southern USA in the 19th century. The original melody is first heard in the piano part at bar 7. A small number of editorial adjustments to dynamics and articulation have been made without comment.

broadening   a tempo

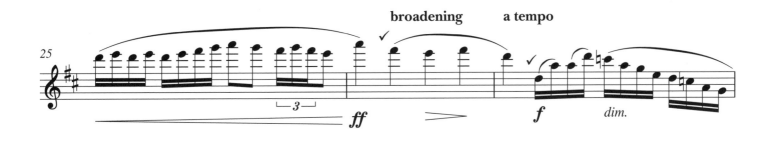

gradually broadening to the end

12

B:3

The Playful Pony

from *Luna's Magic Flute*

Blaž Pucihar
(born 1977)

Blaž Pucihar is a composer and pianist from Slovenia; he leads a quartet which plays the music of Bach in jazz style, and is the director of an international summer school. His wife Ana Kavčič Pucihar is a flautist, and he has written several pieces for her. *Luna's Magic Flute* is a story with music, about a girl named Luna who makes everyone she meets happy by playing her magic flute. 'The Playful Pony' is the music she plays to cheer up a sad pony. When the main tune comes back, in the piano part at the end of bar 75, the flute contributes to the accompaniment: this passage requires a different colour as well as quieter dynamics, all the way to the end of bar 91.

© Copyright 2012 by Pucihar Music
All rights reserved. Reproduced by permission. All enquiries about this piece, apart from those directly relating to the exams, should be addressed to Pucihar Music, Forme 31, 4209 Žabnica, Slovenia.

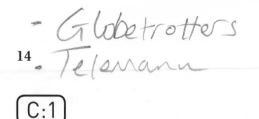

G major
E minors
harmonic (F#D#)
#7
malodic ↑ #6 #7
↓ key signature

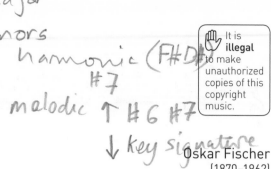

14.

- Globetrotters
- Telemann

C:1

Study in G

Edited by Immanuel Lucchesi

Oskar Fischer
(1870–1962)

Oskar Fischer was a principal flautist in the Leipzig Gewandhaus Orchestra, one of the most famous German orchestras, from 1895 to 1934. He published a tutor and books of studies for the flute. This study is a test of your ability to move easily from one register to another. Watch out for the accents on unexpected beats within phrases! In Lucchesi's edition, the third quaver of bar 39 reads *g*; this has been corrected here to *f*♯.

© Copyright by Deutscher Verlag für Musik, Leipzig
Reproduced by permission. All enquiries about this piece, apart from those directly relating to the exams, should be addressed to Deutscher Verlag für Musik, Bauhofstraße 3–5, D-65195 Leipzig, Germany.

ritard.   **Tempo I**

C:2

Exercise in G

No. 12 from *Schule für Flöte*, Part 2

Edited by Maximilian Schwedler

Ernesto Köhler
(1849–1907)

Allegretto [♩ = c.66]

grazioso

5

9

13

Schule für Flöte Flute Method

Ernesto Köhler was born in the Italian city of Modena when it was part of the Austrian empire. He played the flute in orchestras in the Austrian capital, Vienna, and in the Russian city of St Petersburg. His compositions for his instrument include a Concertino with orchestra, a Grand Quartet for four flutes, numerous pieces with piano accompaniment, and several books of studies. In this study, a repeated phrase is given different articulation each time, so the phrasing and staccatos need to be executed with exceptional clarity. Dynamics, for the most part, are left to the player's discretion. In Schwedler's edition the quaver *d* in bar 2 and bar 6 is printed without the natural sign; a natural sign has been added here by analogy with the same pattern in bars 22 and 26.

C:3

Mango Tango

from *The Modern Flute Player*

Mike Mower
(born 1958)

D.C. al Fine

Mike Mower was born in Bath, in the west of England, and studied the flute at the Royal Academy of Music in London; he also plays the clarinet and saxophone. He was a member of the jazz saxophone quartet Itchy Fingers, and has played and recorded with many leading jazz, rock and classical artists. His 'Mango Tango' is in the rhythm of the Argentinian tango, and some of its phrases suggest the gliding movements of the dance.

© by Itchy Fingers Publications

Reproduced by permission. All enquiries about this piece, apart from those directly relating to the exams, should be addressed to Itchy Fingers Publications, 10 Warminster Road, Beckington, Somerset, BA11 6SY.